When Night Comes
Cuando cae la noche

by Deborah Schecter

ISBN: 978-1-338-70274-3
Illustrated by Anne Kennedy
Copyright © 2020 by Deborah Schecter. All rights reserved.
Published by Scholastic Inc., 557 Broadway, New York, NY 10012

10 9 8 7 6   68   23 24 25 26/0

Printed in Jiaxing, China. First printing, June 2020.

SCHOLASTIC

When night comes,
the mouse comes out.

Cuando cae la noche,
el ratón sale.

When night comes,
the owl comes out.

Cuando cae la noche,
la lechuza sale.

When night comes,
the moth comes out.

Cuando cae la noche,
la mariposa nocturna sale.

When night comes,
the bat comes out.

Cuando cae la noche,
el murciélago sale.

When night comes,
the firefly comes out.

Cuando cae la noche,
la luciérnaga sale.

When night comes,
the cat comes out.

Cuando cae la noche,
el gato sale.

When night comes,
I go inside!

¡Cuando cae la noche,
yo entro!